THIS JOURNAL BELONGS TO:

Rosie

First published in Great Britain in 2017 by Orion Spring,
An imprint of the Orion Publishing group Ltd
Carmelite House
50 Victoria Embankment
London EC4Y 0DZ
An Hachette UK Company

1 3 5 7 9 10 8 6 4 2

A CIP catalogue record for this book is available from the British Library.

ISBN: 9781409176879

Design: Ben Gardiner
Production Controller: Katie Horrocks
Black and white illustrations plus flamingos: Fearne Cotton
All other colour illustrations: Jessica May Underwood
Grey illustrations: Abi Hartshorne

Printed in Italy

FSC
www.fsc.org

MIX
Paper from
responsible sources
FSC® C015829

www.orionbooks.co.uk

ORION
SPRING

FEARNE COTTON

HAPPY

THE JOURNAL

A CHANCE TO WRITE JOY INTO EVERY DAY AND
LET GO OF PERFECT

HELLO!

Welcome to *HAPPY: The Journal*. A place for you to express, wind down, reflect and take stock of all that is rumbling along in your life.

Writing my book *HAPPY* proved to be the most cathartic process of my life. It gave me the opportunity to admit to myself how I truly felt and to open up to others – and in turn connected me with a whole new group of people who engaged with my story. Writing is such a wonderful alchemy of words, truths and vulnerability, and that's what inspired me to turn *HAPPY* into a journal. I personally find notepads and journals extremely soothing as I have a deep need for organisation (and I'm also a bit of a stationery nerd!). Once a list has been made or a thought has been written down I feel like I can make sense of the general craziness in life.

Each time my pen hits paper, I feel the jumble in my head straightening out, clearing space for clarity and calm. I find this makes for a much happier approach to most situations in life, no matter whether it's something that's already happened that is traumatic to recall, or if we're heading towards a situation that we're worrying about in the future.

Having experienced certain spells of darkness in my life, I've tried pretty much every tactic out there to combat lurking feelings of worry or dread, and writing has become my main source of alleviation. Sometimes I don't really know how I feel about a situation until I've started writing. The process opens up a deeper honesty within me and allows me to clearly process and distinguish my thoughts. Writing is my therapy: a calm, magic spell to help relieve the tension that spins around my head.

This simple luxury doesn't just work with huge traumas in life and small, mundane worries – it's also a good way of taking a moment to appreciate the good stuff. Getting the whirlwind of thoughts out of your head and on to the page not only frees up more mental space for the positives in life but also helps you to find and focus on them.

That is what this book is all about. Consider this your portable friend who is ready for action, with lots of blank space for you to make your own. You can make it completely bespoke to you and your life. This book is made of sturdy stuff; it can take your most horrific admissions, it can listen to your most terrifying fears and it can shield the most toe-curling secrets. It won't tell anyone, it won't judge, and it won't make your problems worse. You can tattoo its pages freely and it'll carry that weight for you and help you process what you need to. Enjoy every minute of scrawling on its blankness and reap the benefits along the way!

If you are experiencing a mental health problem of any kind, you can contact Mind.

Website: mind.org.uk

Info line: 03001233393 (open 9am to 6pm, Monday to Friday – except for bank holidays)

Email: info@mind.org.uk

To support the charity, visit mind.org.uk/get-involved.

HOW TO USE
THIS BOOK

Use this book however you like! It's your canvas to do with as you will. If you want to, you can use the pointers and inspiration on each entry to help you reflect on how you're feeling, and to project you in the direction of clarity and happiness. Each month is themed as we move through the year with its changing seasons and moods, concentrating on topics that I've been investigating on my own happiness journey.

You'll also find space to write down whatever you fancy: it could be a diary entry of what happened that day, a thought or concern, or perhaps a small moment that made you smile. It's completely up to you.

At the bottom of each entry is a blank face where you can draw a mouth that depicts how you feel, such as:

Perhaps an inane grin or cheeky smile, maybe a puzzled scorn or downward grimace. Use them to help you access how you've been feeling when looking back over the month.

And at the end of each month you'll find space to look back over the days before and record all the little things you're grateful for and that made you happy.

This book is all about self-care and 'you' time – so dip into its pages as often and for as long as you like. Whilst this book is open it's ALL ABOUT YOU! Have fun and GOOD LUCK!

JANUARY

HELLO New Year! Once the (potential) hangover has passed and the Christmas decorations are down, there lies a whole year ahead of us. This can be very exciting yet totally daunting too. How might we change things from last year? What do we want the next 12 months to look like? It's all up for grabs. January is the perfect time for starting over. The drama and thrill of December is over so we perhaps all feel that bit more peaceful and subdued. We can plot, think and plan to make things happen and manifest our dreams. I usually start my year with a cosmic order list where I state what I will see happening in the next 12 months. I don't write the list as wishes, I write it like it WILL happen. This is not a flash of sweeping arrogance or even expectation, it's more about clearly visualising the dreams I have and putting them out there into the universe. I know that they may not all come to fruition, and I'm acutely aware that life doesn't always pan out how you want it to, but I believe starting your year with a positive mindset and clear head is a good way to make things happen. January is all about moving forward and new- ness. Focus on that feeling of new, of opportunity and excitement, and see where it takes you. Hello January ... let's do this.

1 JANUARY

Time for that cosmic order list. Write out your wish list for the year ahead not as wishes, but as if each one WILL happen. Let's start the year in a positive way.

1) lose weight - gym + eating
2) more self confidence
3) less worrying
4) apply for jobs in advertising/marketing
5) be happy
6) take care of my body

2 JANUARY

Remember: big dreams
might seem scary or out
of reach but visualising
them clearly is the start of
making them happen.

....

....

....

....

....

....

....

.... ☺

3 JANUARY

Last year is so last year.
What are the things you're
going to change going
forward into this new year?

....

....

....

....

....

....

....

....

.... ☺

4 JANUARY

A new year is always the
perfect time to try new
things. Try something –
however small.

· ·

· ·

· ·

· ·

· ·

· ·

· ·

· ·

· ☺

5 JANUARY

Step into this new year
with excitement and turn
fear into adventure.

· ·

· ·

· ·

· ·

· ·

· ·

· ·

· ☺

" NEVER BE
AFRAID TO
START AGAIN.
IT'S A CHANCE
TO REBUILD
YOUR LIFE
THE WAY YOU
WANTED ALL
ALONG "

6 JANUARY

I love writing lists to clear
my overcrowded head.
Write a list of things you
need to do here. It could
be for tomorrow, for the
week or for the whole year
ahead.

....
....
....
....
....
....
....
....
....

7 JANUARY

You're a week into the
new year – how is this new
start making you feel?
Write down your honest
emotions here.

....
....
....
....
....
....
....
....

8 JANUARY

I often get stuck in bad
habits and patterns
and these can be hard
to break. What habits
would you like to break
this month?

....

....

....

....

....

....

....

....

....

9 JANUARY

How are you feeling today?
Draw a picture in the
space below to depict your
current emotions.

10 JANUARY

At times, I feel held back
by self-doubt. I lose my
confidence and this stops
me achieving my goals.
Is there anything holding
you back in life that you
can make a conscious
effort to thwart this year?

....
....
....
....
....
....
....
....

11 JANUARY

Have some YOU time
today. It's so important to
take a break from the chaos
of life to get some simple
solitude and peace. What
does that look like to you?

....
....
....
....
....
....
....
....

12 JANUARY

Don't beat yourself up if you're feeling like things aren't moving quickly enough. I can be terribly impatient about things not moving as fast as I would like. What are you feeling impatient about and can you see a way to wait more peacefully for it to happen?

13 JANUARY

You're doing great! Feel proud of yourself and recognise all your achievements in life so far. What do you feel proud about today?

14 JANUARY

Eat something really
nourishing today. Cook
something from scratch
to nurture your body
and mind.

15 JANUARY

Call someone you have
lost touch with. Is this
the year to rekindle lost
friendships? Who might
that be?

....

....

....

....

....

....

....

16 JANUARY

Accept and embrace
newness with open arms!

....

....

....

....

....

....

....

17 JANUARY

Sleep well. It's easy to get into bad sleeping habits especially if you have kids or if you have to work late/ strange hours. Remember to rest and catch up on zzz's when you can.

· ·

· ·

· ·

· ·

· ·

· ·

· ·

· ·

18 JANUARY

Don't panic. A new year can feel very overwhelming. What are you worried about? Write down those fears and clear them from your mind.

· ·

· ·

· ·

· ·

· ·

· ·

· ·

· ·

19 JANUARY

It's perfectly fine to dream big and have grand goals but just remember you won't miraculously be a new person if you achieve them. The adventure of climbing new mountains and achieving new goals is thrilling but you'll still be you at the end of it. There is no guarantee or pot of gold at the end of the rainbow. Enjoy the journey and remember to enjoy the now!

20 JANUARY

Take a long bath. When it's cold outside there's nothing more therapeutic than a soak in the tub and a good book.

21 JANUARY

Get moving. The new
year is always a good time
to try a new activity. It
could be a new yoga class
or even just meeting up
regularly with a mate to go
for a long walk and a good
gossip.

22 JANUARY

Write down your emotional goals
for the year. It is easy to focus on
work accolades, things we want to
attain or achieve, but we sometimes
forget to try and improve how we
feel about what goes on around
us. Could you react better to
stress? Deal with tricky people in
a calmer way or have more clarity
on decisions that need to be made?
Write those goals down here.

23 JANUARY

If you're feeling a little
scared to try news things,
recall a past adventure
where you were daring and
spontaneous. Write down
how it felt and what you
gained from it.

24 JANUARY

Can you find a comforting recipe to cook today?

....
....
....
....
....
....
....
....
....

25 JANUARY

Do you have any tricky relationships with colleagues, friends or family? How do you think you could help change those relationships for the better? Is there any movement your end?

....
....
....
....
....
....
....
....
....

26 JANUARY

The days are short and nights are long now – can you feel this affecting your mood? Write your thoughts here.

....
....
....
....
....
....
....
....

27 JANUARY

The end of this month can be tricky as the credit card bills flood in! Don't feel alone; open that post and be aware of how it makes you feel.

....
....
....
....
....
....
....
....

28 JANUARY

Relationships with friends, family members and partners can be challenging. Is there something you've been holding back that's causing you pain? Can you write the issue here?

"

DIFFICULT ROADS LEAD TO BEAUTIFUL DESTINATIONS

"

29 JANUARY

Acknowledge how your body is feeling today. Does it feel heavy or light?

....

....

....

....

....

....

....

....

30 JANUARY

Arrange to have a coffee with a friend today. What do you want to talk about?

....

....

....

....

....

....

....

....

31 JANUARY

**THANK YOU
JANUARY FOR ...**

....

....

....

....

....

....

....

....

....

....

....

....

....

....

....

....

....

....

....

FEBRUARY

February. You either love it or you hate it for a couple of reasons. The newness and hope of the new year has faded somewhat, which may relieve you or make you feel lethargic. We also have Valentine's Day on the cards, which will either be a fantastic reason to tell everyone in your circle you love them, or make you feel like crap. There is little grey area with this month. It's all or nothing. SO, how do you wanna play it? We can fall off the wagon completely and surrender to February's dull skies or we can reboot and try again.

As far as Valentine's goes, I have always liked to use it as an excuse to go heavy on the LOVE, even when I've been single and feeling miserable about it. I have always sent my group of best mates cards, sent gooey texts to those I love and also taken a moment to love myself. That is the hardest one for sure. Self-love is tricky and always sounds naff, but my God it's important. We have to start by loving or at least accepting ourselves with all of our quirks and oddities before we can fully love another peacefully. Use this month to focus on that love that is all around you, even if you can't see it right now. Love others, love yourself. Love makes the world go round.

1 FEBRUARY

Welcome to the month of love. What do you love the most?

....
....
....
....
....
....
....
....
.... ⊙⊙

2 FEBRUARY

How do you feel when you are in love?

....
....
....
....
....
....
....
....
.... ⊙⊙

3   FEBRUARY

Who do you love in life and
who are you grateful for?

· ·

· ·

· ·

· ·

· ·

· ·

· ·

· ·

· ⌣

4   FEBRUARY

How much do you think
you love yourself right
now? Sometimes this can
be the hardest challenge
to crack. Self-love can be
complicated.

· ·

· ·

· ·

· ·

· ·

· ·

· ⌣

5   FEBRUARY

Doodle. What does love
look like to you?

6   FEBRUARY

WHAT do you love about
yourself? It can be hard to admit
that we enjoy parts of ourselves.
Reject the misplaced idea that
this is an ego-based exercise
or makes you big-headed – it's
actually one of the healthiest
things you can do. When you
are aware of what your strengths
are and what parts of yourself
you love, others will notice them
much more vividly too.

7 FEBRUARY

Have a day of self-love.
Be kind to yourself. Let
yourself off the hook and
treat yourself.

8 FEBRUARY

Look for love around you.
When we feel down it can
be very tricky to see much
love at all but I promise
it'll be there, somewhere.
There'll be a friend at
the end of the phone, a
relative with a helping
hand, or a neighbour with
a big mug of tea. Look for
it and it'll be there.

9 FEBRUARY

Call someone today that
you love. Tell them you
love them even if there is
no particular occasion to
pin it to.

10 FEBRUARY

See the good in others.
It can be very tricky for
us all to see the good in
those who challenge us
but there will be some.
Recognising this allows
us to see most people out
there fairly.

11 FEBRUARY

Recall a moment that was
full to the brim of pure
love. I love reminiscing
about good times that
were drenched in love.
Happiness floods in.

12 FEBRUARY

Write a love letter to yourself. As sickening as this may sound it is a lovely way to accept your own faults and mishaps, it allows you to nurture the potential that sits dormant and opens you up to receiving that bit more love from others.

DEAR ME, ...

....

....

....

....

....

....

....

....

....

....

....

....

....

13 FEBRUARY

Send a Valentine's Day
card to someone you love
– it could be anyone, not
just your partner or family
member. There's an extra
joy opening snail mail from
a mate. If you really want
to go to town, make one
from scratch and deliver it
in person tomorrow! I love
a handmade card!

14 FEBRUARY

What are your favourite
love songs? They might not
be classic mushy songs but
ones that simply have deep
meaning for you. Write
them down here and play
them loud today, just for
yourself.

YOU OWE
YOURSELF THE
LOVE THAT
YOU SO FREELY
GIVE TO OTHER
PEOPLE

"

15 FEBRUARY

What did you love doing as a kid? Sometimes we let that inner kid take a back seat as there is so much serious stuff to contend with in grown-up life. We can get so bogged down with logistics, goals, bills, drama that we forget to simply have fun. Writing this list may make you realise how much you've lost touch with this side of yourself.

16 FEBRUARY

What foods do you love the most? This would be a long list for me!

17 FEBRUARY

When did you first fall in love and who was it with? Even if it didn't end as you wanted it to, enjoy the fond memories you shared.

· ·

· ·

· ·

· ·

· ·

· ·

· ·

· ☺

18 FEBRUARY

If I'm feeling lonely, I'll hit up a good friend who makes me feel calm and loved. Who is this person for you?

· ·

· ·

· ·

· ·

· ·

· ·

· ·

· ☺

19 FEBRUARY

Can you forgive?
Forgiving someone can be
very tricky but ultimately
it's freedom for you. You
don't have to hold on to
anger, hate or resentment
if you are willing to let
it go. Forgiveness is
freedom.

....

....

....

....

....

....

....

....

.... ☺

20 FEBRUARY

If you've been hurt in a
relationship it can stop
you trusting again. Have
you been hurt before and
if so, how do you think it
has affected you?

....

....

....

....

....

....

....

.... ☺

21 FEBRUARY

We all have things about ourselves we don't like so much. We beat ourselves up and compare ourselves to others. These personal hates can really hold us back as we get so blind-sided by their size. We blow up these shortcomings to supersize proportions and forget about the good stuff. Write a list here of the things you don't like about yourself. It could be personality traits, mistakes you think you've made, body parts, words spoken. Get it all out and know that every one of us has a list like this. Set it free on these pages and then work your way back through the list to see how you might be able to start accepting some of them.

22 FEBRUARY

DON'T TEXT YOUR EX.
It may be tempting but
it will usually only end in
tears. I've done this many a
time when I've been single
and I've usually ended up
feeling so much worse
about myself afterwards.
Delete their phone
number if you need to.

23 FEBRUARY

Can you give a little love
today: your time, an
online donation, a charity
shop run? Showing the
universe a little love will
open you up to 'happy'.

24 FEBRUARY

What room in your home do
you love the most and why?

· ·

· ·

· ·

· ·

· ·

· ·

· ·

· ·

· · · · · · · · · · · · · · · · · · ⊙⊙

25 FEBRUARY

Feel the love. Close your
eyes and visualise all the
love around you.

· ·

· ·

· ·

· ·

· ·

· ·

· ·

· ·

· · · · · · · · · · · · · · · · · · ⊙⊙

26 FEBRUARY

How open does your heart
feel today?

....
....
....
....
....
....
....
....

27 FEBRUARY

The month is nearly over –
write what you are looking
forward to next week. If
you don't have anything
planned yet, write a plan
to do one activity that
brings joy.

....
....
....
....
....
....
....
....

28/29
FEBRUARY

**THANK YOU
FEBRUARY FOR ...**

FEBRUARY

MARCH

So once we've worked out what we want from our year and how we might go about it, we can step back and look at choice. We can work out not only the paths we may tread but also how we choose to react to situations around us. Can we choose happiness? At times we can feel very out of control and like we have no choice at all. We react to people who push our buttons, or feel out of our depth in situations that make us feel uneasy. We must always try to remember we have a choice. We can choose to react from a place that lies in the hands of the past, we can choose to react from a place of pain and hurt, or from a place that lives in the NOW in our hearts. This month is all about remembering we have a choice. That is freeing in itself. Feel that freedom. No matter how big or teeny-tiny those changes of perspective are, or how obscure you personal choices might be, go with your gut and speak from your heart.

1   MARCH

Having choice is the
ultimate freedom, but
sometimes we forget we
have it, especially when
life is challenging – write
down here every tiny choice
you've made today to
remind yourself of that fact.

2   MARCH

One amazing example
of the power of choice is
recognising that we can
choose HOW to react to
situations: in a positive
way, a negative way, or
not at all ... we can walk
away. Can you think of a
current situation and write
one reason here why you
should choose to let go of
the anger or hurt?

3 MARCH

Do you feel stuck in any area of your life?

· ·

· ·

· ·

· ·

· ·

· ·

· ·

· ⊙⊙

4 MARCH

If there is a situation in your life you cannot change, the switch-up will come from you accepting this, rather than butting your head against a wall constantly hoping for something that won't happen.

· ·

· ·

· ·

· ·

· ·

· ·

· ⊙⊙

5   MARCH

Is there a situation
that makes you feel
out of control? Just to
acknowledge it will bring
you strength.

. . . .

. . . .

. . . .

. . . .

. . . .

. . . .

. . . .

. . . . ⊙‿⊙

6   MARCH

Huge change can occur in
the tiniest nuggets of time.

. . . .

. . . .

. . . .

. . . .

. . . .

. . . .

. . . .

. . . . ⊙‿⊙

7 MARCH

Are you finding it hard to make a decision in life? It could be a huge life decision that is causing you sleepless nights or something trivial that is bugging you. No matter its size write it down here:

. . . .

. . . and fill out the Pros and Cons to see which list gains more traction!

PROS   CONS

. . . .

. . . .

. . . .

. . . .

. . . .

. . . .

. . . .

. . . .

. . . .

. . . .

8   MARCH

In my twenties, I had one goal:
to be as successful career-
wise as I could be. I didn't
ever question why I wanted
this or whether it would bring
happiness. My goals have
since massively changed and I
believe succss is doing things
you love. Make sure your goal
is right for you. What do you
want and why?

9   MARCH

Anger is a waste of time
and serves no one. Putting
weighty mind-power
to good use is a much
healthier option and a
great choice in those
moments when we feel
drawn in by the seduction
of ranting or gossip.

10 MARCH

I feel lucky to have a lot of people in my life who choose to have a positive outlook and an open mind, from whom I can constantly learn. List your people here.

. . . .

. . . .

. . . .

. . . .

. . . .

. . . .

. . . .

. . . .

11 MARCH

If you know your inner happiness could improve with change, never be afraid to grab those choices by the horns and breathe in the unknown.

. . . .

. . . .

. . . .

. . . .

. . . .

. . . .

. . . .

. . . .

"

DON'T CALL IT A DREAM, CALL IT A PLAN

"

12 MARCH

For the next seven days, try and make one conscious change each day to remind yourself how powerful choice is and how powerful YOU are. You never know, it could lead somewhere magical! You can think small or big on this one. Here are some ideas:

- Trying a new recipe for dinner.
- Cycling, walking or taking the bus to work rather than driving.
- Talking to a mum at the school gate or colleague at work you've not spoken to before.
- Doing something active at the beginning or end of the day – like swimming, yoga, jogging – that you wouldn't usually do.
- Trying an activity or class you haven't done before (knitting anyone?!).
- Taking a different route to work/the shops.
- Digging out something you haven't worn for years.

MY CHANGE FOR TODAY: . . . .

13 MARCH   **MY CHANGE FOR TODAY:**

. . . .

. . . .

. . . .

. . . .

. . . .

14 MARCH

MY CHANGE FOR TODAY:

· ·

· ·

· ·

· ·

· ·

· ·

· ☺

15 MARCH

MY CHANGE FOR TODAY:

· ·

· ·

· ·

· ·

· ·

· ☺

MARCH

16 MARCH

MY CHANGE FOR TODAY:

....
....
....
....
....
....
....
....
....
....
....
....
....
....
....
....

17 MARCH

MY CHANGE FOR TODAY:

....

....

....

....

....

....

....

18 MARCH

MY CHANGE FOR TODAY:

....

....

....

....

....

....

....

19 MARCH

Look back at the changes you made over the past week – how did they make you feel, did you feel joy? And have you made a change for good?

....

....

....

....

....

....

....

....

20 MARCH

Do you have any bad habits that you would like to change?

....

....

....

....

....

....

....

....

21 MARCH

Write within this outline anything that is making you feel uncomfortable in life. Rather than numbing or burying that feeling or situation, sit with it. Get to know it better, understand it better, and make peace with it.

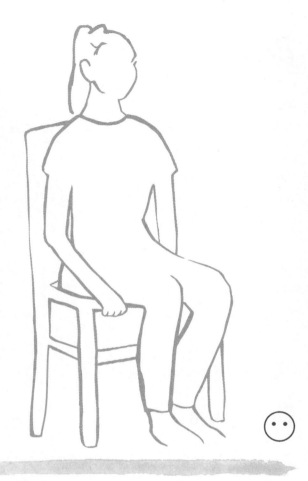

22 MARCH

There are equal measures of magical and wonderful things happening in the world, but we tend to hear more about the negative. When we hear these stories, instead of ranting and getting ourselves physically worked up, we can choose to send a prayer, a good thought, or a wish for those who truly need it.

. . . .

. . . .

. . . .

. . . .

. . . .

. . . .

23 MARCH

Always remember you can make a positive choice to DO something about any events that are upsetting you – you can channel that frustration and energy to do good.

....
....
....
....
....
....
....
....
....

24 MARCH

They key to my happiness is a melting pot of loving, sharing, receiving gratefully, being creative and accepting what is occurring in life. What are your keys to happiness?

....
....
....
....
....
....
....
....

25 MARCH

When I have managed
to take control of a bad
situation and initiate
change, even if it's a tiny
one, I feel safer, more
balanced and happier.

26 MARCH

In today's culture, thinking
positively is almost out of
fashion. We are constantly
reminded of what we
are 'lacking' through
advertising and the need
to compare ourselves to
others. Focusing on the
positives, and learning to
accept the parts of life we
can't change, will lead us
to a happier life.

27 MARCH

If you're seeing a big life change on the horizon but still can't quite take a leap into the unknown, for now, take small considered steps. You don't have to make a great splash from the get-go.

28 MARCH

We can mould our own story if we choose. On the first half of this page, write down what happened today . . .

. . . on the second half, imagine if you'd done a few things differently and the changes that would have occurred as a result. Remembering that we have choice is so empowering.

29 MARCH

If you know there is room
for change, then what
is stopping you? Fear?
Other people's opinions?
Lack of confidence? If you
know making a change will
lead you to unlocking your
inner happiness then GO
FOR IT. Today!

30 MARCH

Change is incredibly
powerful when we all get
together. More people
thinking in a certain way
and wanting change can
move mountains.

31 MARCH

**THANK YOU
MARCH FOR ...**

....

....

....

....

....

....

....

....

....

....

....

....

....

....

....

....

....

....

MARCH

APRIL

We are by now in the throes of spring and all feel we are awakening from a sleepy winter. We can shake off those woolly socks and cardigans and stretch up to the sunny skies. Time for a detox. I'm not talking about drinking excessive amounts of fresh juice or having a daily colonic; I'm talking about a full-throttle life clear out. Start with your head and its array of thoughts. Which ones no longer serve you? Get rid of bad patterns and habits and step into spring with refreshing clarity. Clear out your home and let go of objects, clothes and possessions you know are cluttering or blocking emotions and not helping you out in life. Clear people from your life that feel toxic and debilitating. It's time for clarity and calm, so clear out the old and be ready and open for the new.

1 APRIL

You're no fool. Don't ever let anyone make you feel like one.

2 APRIL

Have a clear-out. This is my favourite thing to do. More space at home, more clarity and room for newness. New ideas, new thoughts and new energy!

3 APRIL

Have a clothes-swapping party or give your old unwanted possessions to a charity shop. WIN-WIN!

. . . .
. . . .
. . . .
. . . .
. . . .
. . . .
. . . .
. . . .

4 APRIL

Look through your wardrobe and see what clothes you're hanging on to for emotional reasons. If an item of clothing doesn't fill you with joy, then pass it on. Give some joy to someone else.

. . . .
. . . .
. . . .
. . . .
. . . .
. . . .
. . . .

"THE FIRST STEP
TO GETTING
WHAT YOU
WANT IS
HAVING THE
COURAGE TO
GET RID OF
WHAT YOU
DON'T WANT "

5 APRIL

Move furniture around
today. You don't need
to buy new stuff to feel
differently about a room,
and simply moving things
around can bring a fresh
feel to your favourite room.

. . . .
. . . .
. . . .
. . . .
. . . .
. . . .
. . . .
. . . .

6 APRIL

Which room in your house
needs a spruce-up or
clear-out? Can you list
some things you know
could be easily changed
and achieved?

. . . .
. . . .
. . . .
. . . .
. . . .
. . . .
. . . .
. . . .

7 APRIL

Does your head feel fit to burst sometimes? So many thoughts, ideas and things you need to do. Write a list of everything whirring around in your head now. It will reduce any panic you might be feeling.

APRIL

8 APRIL

Are there people in your life you think make things trickier for you, who cause you hurt or make you feel uncomfortable? Is there a chance you could explain how their actions make you feel? Now, at my age, I feel I have fewer friends but the right gang for me. A core group of people I know I can trust, lean on and have great fun with. Happiness is quality not quantity.

9 APRIL

What emotional baggage do you think you carry around with you? Are there past moments you wish to let go of? Draw and name the luggage here.

10 APRIL

Life laundry needn't be too scary or daunting. Slowly look around at your life and wash out what no longer serves you.

11 APRIL

Do you often feel overwhelmed by life? I do when I'm trying to chase my tail with family life and the kids. I end up getting run-down and knackered. During these times, I try to strip everything back to the basics. I'll go to bed early, eat well and also ask for help. Is there anyone who can help lighten your load? If not, can you do less over the next seven days?

12 APRIL

As the saying goes, less is more. It couldn't be more relevant to this month. Strip back to what you know you love in life and keep things simple.

13 APRIL

Try a digital detox today. Why don't you put your phone down for the whole evening and just doodle here instead?

14 APRIL

If your mind feels jumbled
and you know there
are constant thoughts
whirring around your
head, perhaps this could
be the time to try some
meditation. If you can't
manage the solitude in
silence, try listening to a
guided meditation online.

15 APRIL

Is there an ongoing situation in your life that you know you need to extract yourself from? Sometimes we can't as we are bound by blood, geography or circumstance, but are there any ways you can change your approach to this situation?

16 APRIL

How does your diet differ when you are stressed? If you know stress changes how you eat, can you identify the triggers and protect yourself from them?

17 APRIL

Try cutting out refined sugar for a day. It will clarify your relationship with the white stuff. When the 4pm slump hits, reach for fruit first and see how it makes you feel.

18 APRIL

Draw a T-shirt in the box to the right and personalise it with YOUR life message – happiness is catching.

19 APRIL

As I have two kids and two stepkids my house can get very busy with toys, clothes, school stuff, and more stuff! Clearing a small space which is just for you is magic. My bedroom is my haven where I can switch off and feel the space around me.

....
....
....
....
....
....
....
....................................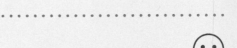

20 APRIL

Which food makes you feel energised and calm?

....
....
....
....
....
....
....
....................................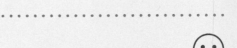

21 APRIL

We all have memories or situations that feel traumatic to recall. We bury them deep and try to forget, only for them to then jump out from the dark when we least expect. Here is the chance to acknowledge, accept and make peace with them.

What memory or thought brings discomfort to you?

> ## SAFE
>
>
>
>
> ## SPACE

Which *one* word describes how this makes you feel?

. . . .

And what one thing, even if very tiny, do you feel you've *learned* from that experience?:

. . . .

When this feeling or memory creeps up again try and *shortcut to the lesson*. That is the bit you can take away with your head held high. We can't make bad times disappear but we can shift our perspective to look at the tiny *silver lining* if we choose.

APRIL

22 APRIL

For the next week, let go
of the negative habits that
are holding you back from
joy. List one each day and
see if you can let let it go.

DAY 1

. . . .

. . . .

. . . .

. . . .

. . . .

. . . .

. . . .

. . . . ⊙‿⊙

23 APRIL

DAY 2

. . . .

. . . .

. . . .

. . . .

. . . .

. . . .

. . . . ⊙‿⊙

24 APRIL

DAY 3

....

....

....

....

....

....

....

....

.... ☺

25 APRIL

DAY 4

....

....

....

....

....

....

....

....

.... ☺

26 APRIL

DAY 5

....

....

....

....

....

....

....

....

.... ⊙‿⊙

---

27 APRIL

DAY 6

....

....

....

....

....

....

....

.... ⊙‿⊙

"

ELIMINATE WHAT DOESN'T HELP YOU EVOLVE

"

28 APRIL

DAY 7

....

....

....

....

....

....

....

.... ⊙⊙

29 APRIL

Colours are part of
our environment and
our surroundings bring
happiness. What's your
happy colour? Plan here
how you can introduce
more into your home.

....

....

....

....

....

....

....

.... ⊙⊙

30 APRIL

THANK YOU
APRIL FOR ...

. . . .
. . . .
. . . .
. . . .
. . . .
. . . .
. . . .
. . . .
. . . .
. . . .
. . . .
. . . .
. . . .
. . . .
. . . .
. . . .
. . . .
. . . .

APRIL

MAY

Now we've tackled that first part of the year it's time to go that little bit deeper. Our minds are complicated beasts, full of non-stop dialogues, strange habits picked up along the way and – at times – negative dispositions. We can put too much focus on how we physically feel, look and move and the poor old brain gets left behind. We assume it'll tick along just fine and do not always pick up on its cries for help and attention. This is the month to stop and make an inventory of how you feel mentally. It is also time to switch off mentally, which can almost feel impossible. We all move at insane speeds these days with work, family life, social engagements and online activity. Our brains need a vacation from it all to carry on working in this way and with such velocity. May is all about giving ourselves some mental space to recharge and rejuvenate. The mind needs to be idle at times, so it can work efficiently the rest of the time. Being 'mindful' or 'awake' is so important to mental wellbeing.

1 MAY

A lot of the time we forget the mind is something we have an element of control over. It's easy to feel it's running the show, but we create our own story, and it doesn't have to go in just one direction.

2 MAY

We all have certain character traits and hold on to those labels tightly. For example, we may be sensitive to criticism, or perhaps we feel overwhelmed when faced with certain tasks. We need reminding that we can shake up our own internal system – we have that power whenever we please. What do you consider your inherent traits? Are there any you'd like to change?

3 MAY

We can feel in control of
our own destinies when
our minds are working
not single-handedly, but
as part of our whole body
and soul.

....
....
....
....
....
....
....
.... ☺

4 MAY

It's hard to make good
decisions when all of the
cogs are turning with
thousands of ideas, thoughts
and concerns. Your mind
needs to stop and bliss out
for a bit so it can work at its
optimum speed when you
really need it to. Without
the pauses, you can't feel
what's really going on.

....
....
....
....
....
....
.... ☺

5   MAY

Getting your mind into good healthy habits, like we do physically with our bodies, is integral, and requires daily practice. You can flex that muscle in whichever way feels right for you. The hurdle is getting your mind to stop. It needs to recharge and go blank for some much-needed breathing space and clarity. For the next week try these mind-blanking activities.

ACTIVITY 1: DOODLING.
Doodling can have a great effect on the mind, as you subconsciously pour your inner thoughts onto a scrap of paper and let those thoughts live and breathe outside your mind. Use the space here to scribble whatever you like.

6 MAY

ACTIVITY 2: HOLLIE'S GUIDED MEDIATION

Hollie de Cruz is a hypnobirthing expert who helped me through my labour. Here is a meditation I still use to help me get to sleep at night or to take five minutes on if I'm on the train to work.

So just close your eyes, and before you begin to relax, take a moment to make yourself comfortable, and feel free to change position at any time if you need to. Begin now to tune in with your own breath, and on an exhale that feels good for you, let your shoulders soften and give yourself permission to relax.

Breathe fully, and breathe deeply. Inhaling peace, and exhaling tension. Let the breath flow all the way down through your chest and your stomach. Let it drift all the way down your legs until you feel the soft tingling of relaxation reach the soles of your feet.

Return your attention now to your eyes – feel how comfortable they have become, and feel now that relaxation spread all across your forehead and your temples. Feel all the little worry lines just fade and disappear, and if you are holding a frown, just easily release it and notice how good that feels. And now feel that wonderful deep relaxation spread on down over your nose and your cheeks, all the way down to your mouth and your jaw. Take a moment to place your tongue behind your upper teeth, and allow your lower jaw to relax, as you drift deeper, and still deeper into this wonderful state of calm relaxation.

With every breath, you allow yourself to relax even more deeply, and on your next exhale, just let your shoulders gently sink into the frame of your body, and feel how relaxed and limp they have become. Your body feels entirely relaxed and at ease, and you feel all tension and worry just drifting away.

And now in your mind's eye, and your imagination, I want you to visualise a beautiful blue sky, and take yourself to your favourite spot in nature. This could be a place from your childhood, a spot that you are fond of now, or perhaps even a place that only exists in your imagination. See yourself here. This is a place where you feel totally safe and secure. A place where there is no tension or worry. A place where you can enjoy the wonderful feeling of being yourself. So safe and secure.

Look around you, take in all of the things around you. Notice what you are standing on – perhaps it is dry grass, or maybe warm sand – notice what this feels like on your bare feet. Be aware of the sounds around you too. Maybe you can hear birds singing, or trees blowing gently in the breeze, or maybe the sound of water trickling down a stream, or the sea gently lapping up against the shore. These sounds make you feel calm, connected and at peace. They make you feel safe. I want you to notice now what the warmth of the sun feels like on your skin. Maybe you can feel its warm golden glow just softly soothing every part of you.

And now, as you visualise the numbers from ten down to one, I want you to feel that warmth just gradually drifting down your body, allowing you to go deeper and deeper into this wonderful state of calmness and relaxation.

So beginning to count now. Ten . . . you can feel that warmth wash down over your head and face, nine . . . feeling the light spread into your neck and your shoulders as they gently relax, eight . . . and all the way down your arms, allowing your elbows to feel relaxed and limp, seven . . . feeling this calming energy flow into your hands, and all the way into your fingertips as they gently rest in your lap or by your sides, six . . . letting that golden light travel down through your chest and your stomach, five . . . breathing light and love down to your very core, four . . . feeling the warmth softly relax your pelvis and all around your hips, releasing all tension, three . . . light travelling down the tops of your legs and all around your knees, two . . . feeling that soft tingling sensation of relaxation reaching the soles of your feet and the tips of your toes, and one . . . feeling completely and wonderfully relaxed, free of all cares and worries, happy and peaceful.

You may continue to rest here, enjoying the wonderful sense of relaxation that softly penetrates every part of you, and knowing that you can access this place of quiet whenever you need to.

Remember that all you need to do to achieve this sense of peace and calmness is to make yourself comfortable and tune in to your own breath – inhaling peace and exhaling tension. As you do, you'll begin to let go and continue to drift into this place of deep relaxation. Each time you practise, it becomes easier and easier to reach this deeply relaxed state.

So now, continue to rest, to breathe, to relax – allowing your mind and your body to take the break they deserve. Know that right now, nobody wants anything – nobody needs anything – there is absolutely nothing to do but relax and let go.

Learning to relax like this will manifest into your ordinary everyday life, and you will enjoy this wonderful new sense of calmness and confidence. You will find it so easy to cope with the stresses and strains of everyday life, because you now know how to relax, and you can access your new skill whenever you need to.

Now I want you to count from one up to five. When you reach five you will open your eyes and bring your awareness back to the room, feeling mentally alert, physically energised, and emotionally calm and confident.

7 MAY

ACTIVITY 3: GO FOR A WALK

– walking and focusing on your every step rather than looking at your phone for the whole journey can help you zone out.

....
....
....
....
....
....
....
.... ☺

8 MAY

ACTIVITY 4: COOKING

– creative flow is so important and doesn't have to be too planned or overthought. I haven't had much time to paint since my children were born so I've channelled my creative flow into baking and cooking. This sort of creative flow has the added benefit of edible results for all to enjoy!

....
....
....
....
....
....
....
.... ☺

9 MAY

ACTIVITY 5: MUSIC
– being skilled at playing an instrument is a creative outlet that takes time and practice, but once you nail it you can switch off mentally and enjoy what your muscles and mind have retained through repetition. I envy this skill my husband so naturally has. If you can't play an instrument then do as I do and listen to your fave piece of music.

10 MAY

ACTIVITY 6: COLOURING
– putting pen or brush to paper releases all sorts of hypnotic qualities that leap forward once you open your mind. The freedom of art is to be explored and taken advantage of.

11 MAY

ACTIVITY 7: GO OUTSIDE

– even if it's just standing on your doorstep, look up at the sky and breathe in deeply through your nose and out through your mouth, and repeat, allowing your mind to drift away.

12 MAY

Making decisions, feeling emotions, speaking the truth, loving wholly, acting authentically, all come from using the WHOLE of you. Your mind, body, and that extra bit of magic you can't quite put your finger on. We have to align all these elements of who we are in order to make the decisions we know deep down will benefit us.

13 MAY

Tell your brain what to do. So many of us spend hours on social media every day even though deep down it can make us feel a bit shit. We tell ourselves: 'This is just what you do every day, get over it.' Make a change. Stop looking at something that makes you feel bad. Get your mind and body feeling good. instead.

....
....
....
....
....
....
....
....

14 MAY

Light attracts light. When I'm feeling negative I know that by habit I tend to seek out more negativity. I forget that I can smile rather than scowl, and I can look for the beauty in what is going on around me, rather than seeing just the darkness.

....
....
....
....
....
....
....
....

15 MAY

Today when you're making
something to eat, really
notice any action you're
doing. There's something
so cathartic about grating
a carrot or whisking
an egg, that repetitive
movement and simple
physical action that
triggers the brain to quiet
down and remain calm.

16 MAY

Whatever your feel-good
happy needs are, make sure
you find them and go with
them. Be in the moment,
lean into the good times
and stare up at the stars.

LIGHT ATTRACTS LIGHT

17 MAY

Simple moments in life can be injected with a shot of grandeur and importance by turning them into rituals. For me, this is making my morning coffee. I take my time and enjoy each step of making it – it makes the end result all the more delicious. Write down what your own ritual is or could be, and each individual step within it.

18 MAY

How does your mind feel today? Don't be afraid to be totally honest.

19 MAY

I'm never on the ball when I'm deprived of sleep and have a shorter temper and less empathy for others. Keep a bedtime diary for the next seven days, logging how many hours you're getting per night; if it's less than seven or eight, see if you can pull it back by the end of the week. If you like, you could keep a dream diary too. Good luck!

DAY 1

. . . .

. . . .

. . . .

. . . .

. . . .

. . . .

. . . .

20 MAY

DAY 2

. . . .

. . . .

. . . .

. . . .

. . . .

. . . .

. . . .

. . . .

. . . .

21 MAY

DAY 3

· ·

· ·

· ·

· ·

· ·

· ·

· ·

· ·

· ☺

22 MAY

DAY 4

· ·

· ·

· ·

· ·

· ·

· ·

· ·

· ☺

23 MAY

DAY 5

....
....
....
....
....
....
....
....
.... ⊙‿

24 MAY

DAY 6

....
....
....
....
....
....
....
.... ⊙‿

MAY

25 MAY

DAY 7

· ·

· ·

· ·

· ·

· ·

· ·

· ·

· ·

· ·

26 MAY

A week ago you wrote
down how your mind
was feeling. Does it feel
differently today? Never
be afraid to explore
exactly how you are truly
feeling, and how this is
changing over time.

· ·

· ·

· ·

· ·

· ·

· ·

· ·

· ·

27 MAY

I know how delicate my mind can be so I try to steer away from unnecessary negativity where I can. I don't watch scary or violent films and I don't go on websites that only feature negative gossip. I like to read books that feel inspiring, watch films that feed my brain with either laughter or stories I can learn from. I want to surround myself with people who talk from the heart and are as willing to share their story, as I am mine. These are the parts of my life I have control over and the ones I can make a choice about. They are all changeable parts of your life, too. Write down any feel-good changes you'd like to make to your own life below.

Negative things in my life   How I can make them positive/do something else

. . . .

. . . .

. . . . ◉‿

28 MAY

Let go today with roars of laughter. Listening to a funny podcast or watching a hilarious film can be equally as powerful as meditating and reflecting.

. . . .

. . . .

. . . .

. . . .

. . . .

. . . .

. . . . ◉‿

29 MAY

We can adapt and change our habits and thought processes whenever we want to – a liberating epiphany that I regularly stumble upon. Aha! I can change. Freedom! Once we recognise this, we can start to steer our lives in whatever direction we desire.

....
....
....
....
....
....
....
....
....

30 MAY

Never be afraid to ask for help. It's the gateway to new ways of thinking and new paths, as energies shift.

....
....
....
....
....
....
....
....

31 MAY

**THANK YOU
MAY FOR ...**

....

....

....

....

....

....

....

....

....

....

....

....

....

....

....

....

....

....

....

MAY

JUNE

Summertime *panic*: we might have to slip into a swimming cossie or bikini and be seen by other humans in our imperfect glory! Summertime can feel daunting and exposing as social media is drenched with tanned, lithe bodies slipping out of swimming pools in front of killer sunsets. I have a wonderfully wobbly stretched tummy from having two babies as well as very pasty skin that doesn't see much daylight – but this month is NOT about diets and fake tanning, it's about acceptance. Giving yourself permission to love your body as it is and to not feel judged or compared by others. This means we too have to stop comparing our-selves to others, which can be tough. June is about eating well to feel physically great but also about accepting we might not be Gisele by the end of the month even if we pop to Barry's Boot Camp once a week. It's about approaching things YOUR way. Whether that means going to yoga, the odd run, walking to work in the morning, or simply going out dancing with your mates, move your body in a way that makes you FEEL good. Drop the constant thoughts of physical results and aim to feel amazing, vibrant and happy in the whole of you. Be kind to yourself and love your body and what it can do.

1   JUNE

With the combination
of our gargantuan mind-
power and the strength
of our human body, we
can achieve so much, or
so very little.

2   JUNE

Some days, I can calm my
physical side with good
thoughts and a positive
mindset but equally I can
quiet my mind with slow
and considered physical
movements. Body and
mind can work alongside
each other and also help
each other out.

" IF ONLY OUR EYES SAW SOULS INSTEAD OF BODIES, HOW VERY DIFFERENT OUR IDEALS OF BEAUTY WOULD BE "

3 JUNE

It all starts with gratitude for our bodies, something I had very little of growing up. Now I am in awe of the human body. It is an incredible machine that is unrivalled by any invention. It can self-heal, grow, change, move and create, but we have to love it first. So tomorrow we're going to kick off 'Be kind to yourself' week! Let's do it.

4 JUNE

BE KIND TO YOURSELF – DAY 1

It may seem slightly odd to talk to yourself in the mirror but, hey, if it helps, WHY NOT? Try giving yourself a pep-talk today to boost your confidence and to make you stop and realise how bloody brilliant you are.

5 JUNE

BE KIND TO YOURSELF – DAY 2

If I have a big job ahead that I'm nervous about, I will often come up with a little mantra that I will repeat in my head, such as, 'I am strong and capable and will spread happiness with my words.' Planting these thoughts in our subconscious really makes a difference to our actions.

....
....
....
....
....
....
....
....
....

6 JUNE

BE KIND TO YOURSELF – DAY 3

Congratulate yourself. We're a nation of self-deprecators, but today is all about recognising how brilliant you are. Write down everything you are proud of, but specifically think of amazing things your body has done for you over the years.

....
....
....
....
....
....
....
....

7 JUNE

BE KIND TO YOURSELF – DAY 4

We all abuse and neglect our body at some point in our lives and all make conscious efforts to be kind to it at others. Here is your chance to reflect on what your body has been through in life so far and show thanks and respect to it. Write your own 'Dear Body' letter here:

DEAR BODY, ...

....

....

....

....

....

....

....

....

....

....

....

....

8   JUNE

BE KIND TO YOURSELF
– DAY 5

Like yourself. If there are any of your
body parts that you're not too keen on,
for whatever reason, address that now!
No matter what wobbly bits or parts
of us we view as strange, or stretch
marks or mummy scars we might have,
our bodies do amazing things each and
every day. See the positives in your
body – it has got you this far.

....
....
....
....
....
....
....
.... ☺

9   JUNE

BE KIND TO
YOURSELF – DAY 6

Have a bath. (Or a long
shower – or whatever
equals 'me' time to you.)
Give your body its own
pat-on-the-back by
having a good soothing
soak in the tub. Candles
and Netflix are optional!

....
....
....
....
....
....
....
.... ☺

10 JUNE

BE KIND TO
YOURSELF
– DAY 7

Be kind to yourself – literally.
We are all our own worst critics
– but we can be our own best
advocates too. Any time you
feel like criticising yourself
today, let the angel on your
shoulder talk back and silence
that inner critic.

11 JUNE

It's strange that the
negative is usually so much
louder than the positive.
It shouts from above in a
gravelly, alarming tone.
Positivity seems to have a
gentle whisper that can get
drowned out or taken for
granted. But that's because
it doesn't need to shout
or stomp about. It is self-
assured and grounded.

12 JUNE

Remember that what your body gives you depends on how you're treating it. I can't expect to have a great night's sleep physically if my mind is racing 100 miles per hour. I can't expect to get out of a dark hole emotionally if I've been drinking lots of gin and not eating properly. Your mind and body need to support each other.

13 JUNE

I aim, both mentally and physically, to avoid excessive rushes of adrenaline and to embrace the peace and balance that I would have previously found 'boring'. What works for me now is having calm in my mind and my body so it can grow and function and heal as needed. Don't be afraid of feeling a change within yourself.

14 JUNE

Being active makes me feel alive. It can shift mental struggles while simultaneously charging my body with strength and energy. I'm sure many of you work in an office where you feel numb from sitting at your desk all day. You might be full-time parents with no time to stop and think about your own needs. Some of you might feel you're coping just fine without any exercise in your daily lives, but I really believe that a bit of movement doesn't have to cost an arm and a leg and there are clever ways to fit it around what you do daily.

So I'm declaring the next seven days 'walking week'. All you need for this is your legs, (potentially an umbrella), and a pedometer – you can download loads for free on app stores. You don't have to do this, of course, but it won't cost you anything, so give it a go if you can.

Aim to squeeze in at least 10,000 steps by picking one or more of the ideas below – or make up your own if you like!

- Walk to work.
- Walk your kids to school.
- Get off the bus/tube/train one stop early and walk the rest of the way.
- When you boil the kettle, do a lap of the office/house.
- Make an outing of it: take a picnic and go for a long one.
- Pick a pub a couple of miles away for an incentive!
- Do a lap of your village/street in the morning and/or the evening.
- Dance around your kitchen when you're waiting for the dinner to cook (for when it's pouring so hard you can't possibly go outside!).

WALKING WEEK:

DAY 1

STEPS WALKED:

JUNE

15 JUNE

WALKING WEEK:
DAY 2

STEPS WALKED:

· · · · · · · · · · · · · · · · · · ·

· ·
· ·
· ·
· ·
· ·
· ·
· ·
· ⊙‿⊙

---

16 JUNE

WALKING WEEK:
DAY 3

STEPS WALKED:

· · · · · · · · · · · · · · · · · · ·

· ·
· ·
· ·
· ·
· ·
· ·
· ⊙‿⊙

17 JUNE

WALKING WEEK:
DAY 4

STEPS WALKED:

· · · · · · · · · · · · · · · · · · ·

· ·
· ·
· ·
· ·
· ·
· ·
· ·
· ☺

18 JUNE

WALKING WEEK:
DAY 5

STEPS WALKED:

· · · · · · · · · · · · · · · · · · ·

· ·
· ·
· ·
· ·
· ·
· ·
· ☺

"

YOU CAN'T POUR FROM AN EMPTY CUP. TAKE CARE OF YOURSELF FIRST

"

19 JUNE

WALKING WEEK:
DAY 6

STEPS WALKED:

· · · · · · · · · · · · · · · · · ·

....
....
....
....
....
....
....
....
.... ☺

20 JUNE

WALKING WEEK:
DAY 7

STEPS WALKED:

· · · · · · · · · · · · · · · · · ·

....
....
....
....
....
....
....
....
.... ☺

21 JUNE

Body language is a really powerful tool that you can use to help you feel confident and happy – eventually your mindset will catch up with your body and be onboard with this new-found confidence. If we walk into a room, and inside we are feeling quite vulnerable and nervous, our body language often seems small and inward. If we trick our minds by letting our bodies tell a different story, others pick up on these signals and will be drawn to our perceived confidence and presence in the room. Maybe when you were younger you managed to blag your way into a club by physically holding yourself in a confident and empowering way? This is exactly the same thinking.

For the next five days, when you get up in the morning, take two whole minutes to do a powerful pose. I like to do a starfish – with my legs wide and my arms out straight and my chest puffed out. Or you could stand with your hands on your hips with your feet a hips' distance apart – so long as it's a stance that makes you feel powerful. Keep a note of how it makes you feel, and whether you notice any changes in your behaviour during that day.

POWER POSE DAY 1

. . . .

. . . .

. . . .

. . . .

. . . .

. . . .

. . . .

22 JUNE

POWER POSE DAY 2

....
....
....
....
....
....
....
....
.... ☺

23 JUNE

POWER POSE DAY 3

....
....
....
....
....
....
....
.... ☺

24 JUNE

POWER POSE DAY 4

· ·
· ·
· ·
· ·
· ·
· ·
· ·
· ·
· ⊙‿⊙

---

25 JUNE

POWER POSE DAY 5

· ·
· ·
· ·
· ·
· ·
· ·
· ·
· ⊙‿⊙

26 JUNE

How are you feeling today?

HAPPY	SAD	SPARKY
ENERGISED	LOW	OVERWHELMED
EXCITED	BOUNCY	NUMB
JOYFUL	DRENCHED	PRICKLY
FRUITY	HEAVY	STUCK
LOVING	CONFUSED	TIRED
SCARED	BUBBLY	FRAGILE

. . . .

. . . .

27 JUNE

Dance like no one is watching to your favourite song of the moment. As the music finishes, write down how it made you feel.

. . . .

. . . .

. . . .

. . . .

. . . .

. . . .

. . . .

. . . .

28 JUNE

How simple is breathing?
Breath is so powerful.
Long, deep and steady
breaths level out our
nervous systems and calm
our every cell while pulling
the mind back to a gentle
wave of consciousness.
This is my happy place!
And I hope it can be
yours, too.

29 JUNE

Be nice to yourself. Thank
your body and see the
good in it, every day.

30 JUNE

**THANK YOU
JUNE FOR ...**

. . . .

. . . .

. . . .

. . . .

. . . .

. . . .

. . . .

. . . .

. . . .

. . . .

. . . .

. . . .

. . . .

. . . .

. . . .

. . . .

. . . .

. . . .

JUNE

JULY

This month can be awfully exciting. Perhaps a little holiday, maybe some fun outdoor birthday parties or a weekend at a music festival. The possible heat, summer clothes and sense of adventure can be quietly intoxicating and a lot of fun. I love this month and always try to let go that bit more whilst focusing on the mantra 'you only live once'. What I sometimes forget to bear in mind is balance. This is when I usually reach my personal limit and feel I'm fit to burst. I am chasing my tail with family life, my job and trying to socialise on top of it all. I tend to get run-down in these moments, which gives me no choice but to take a look at how I'm dividing up my time. Use this month to gain balance in it all. There is room for all of it: fun, work, family and adventure. But we have to know our own limits and also have priorities. For me, it'll always be work and family, but this month allows me to dive into fun a little more as it's everywhere. Your balance might be partying that bit too much and you know that there is room for more rest and downtime. Maybe your work-life balance is a little off and you know you need more time at home. Work out your own inner barometer and listen to what it is telling you. When we are balanced it's always easier to access that inner happiness.

1 JULY

How do you feel at
the moment? Is there
anything that feels out of
balance: your emotions,
your body, your spirit?

2   JULY

We may feel like we have
no time in the day but
we can all make small
changes to loosen this up
somewhat. Try these seven
tiny ideas to help you
mentally press 'pause' over
the next seven days.

....

....

....

....

....

....

....

....

3   JULY

IDEA 1
Turn your phone off in the
evening. Choose a time
that feels right for you
and make sure you don't
go back on your digital
curfew until breakfast the
next day.

....

....

....

....

....

....

....

....

4   JULY

IDEA 2

Take time when you eat.
Make sure you chew and
enjoy every mouthful fully.

. . . .
. . . .
. . . .
. . . .
. . . .
. . . .
. . . .
. . . .

5   JULY

IDEA 3

Stand outside for five
minutes come rain or
shine. I love to fling open
my front door, stand
under the stars (or clouds)
at night and breath in
some good old-fashioned
fresh air. It's like smoking,
without the smoking.

. . . .
. . . .
. . . .
. . . .
. . . .
. . . .
. . . .
. . . .

6 JULY

IDEA 4

Get back to simplicity
with an activity that
doesn't require your
phone. Draw a picture
of what balance feels
like for you.

7 JULY

IDEA 5

Be fully in the present and
take a real look around
you. You can be in the
busiest of environments
and still feel really calm
if you stop and observe
the scene. Listen to the
sounds, sense the quality
of air and breathe in your
clothes' washing powder
scent.

JULY

8 JULY

IDEA 6

Count to fifty. I try to cram so much into each day that sometimes I rush through everything. This causes clumsiness and lack of awareness. If we stop here and there, and count and breathe, we can get back to a more calming pace.

9 JULY

IDEA 7
Be silent for a moment.
Listen to your inner voice
and write down one thing
you really want to do
today.

....
....
....
....
....
....
....
....
....

10 JULY

Achieving balance in your
life has to be a personal
project. I really believe
you have a choice to
either compare your life
to others' or not. You must
decide how to devote
your own time and energy
without envying or judging
others.

....
....
....
....
....
....
....
....
....

11 JULY

Our days are short but there is usually some room for movement if you're willing to sacrifice a little of something else. Rest and stopping has to take priority at times. I'm useless at it so I'm repeating this to remind you and me!

....
....
....
....
....
....
....
....
.... ☺

12 JULY

Deep breaths are like little love notes to your body.

....
....
....
....
....
....
....
....
.... ☺

"

YOU CAN DO ANYTHING, BUT NOT EVERYTHING

"

13 JULY

It's all about finding those short periods of time when you allow yourself space to breathe, time to heal, recharge and be still. Allow yourself to BE and not DO. After all, we are human BEings not DOings.

....
....
....
....
....
....
....
....
.... ⊙‿⊙

14 JULY

Do you feel unbalanced emotionally? Do you fly off the handle at small problems or cry over the mundane? Can you gain any perspective on these moments or see how you can bring balance back?

....
....
....
....
....
....
....
....
.... ⊙‿⊙

15 JULY

Extracting ourselves from
the everyday hamster
wheel of life gives us
space to think outside
of our comfort zone and
perhaps be a little more
courageous.

....
....
....
....
....
....
....
....
....

16 JULY

Avoiding drama is essential
on our pilgrimage to the land
of balance and happiness.
Surface-level judgements
only attract the same back,
so now I try and remember
my own tough times and
mistakes so I don't judge
others so much.

....
....
....
....
....
....
....
....
....

17   JULY

Sometimes there is
the sort of hassle or
upset that arrives in
your life unbidden and
unexpectedly. When it
happens, protect yourself,
and your heart, by
navigating your way out of
it with the least possible
damage. Self-care is so
important.

18 JULY

If I'm in a tetchy mood and feeling
dramatic myself, I know certain
people I can call or meet up with
who will send me spiraLling off
further. With that self-knowledge, I
try to turn to people who will fill me
with level-headed common sense
and balancing advice. If you have
a calm person in your life like this,
write their name down here, then
how they make you feel.

. . . .

. . . .

. . . .

. . . .

. . . .

. . . .

. . . .

. . . . ⊙⊙

19 JULY

Top of my priority list in terms of what
makes me feel good is hanging out with
my kids and husband, and work. The next
rung down on the ladder is for friends
and activities that fall into the daytime
hours. Going out at night, like I did in
my twenties, has fallen off the priority
ladder altogether at the moment. I have
CHOSEN not to give it energy for now.
Write down your own priority list here .
Can you let go of the FOMO?

. . . .

. . . .

. . . .

. . . .

. . . .

. . . .

. . . .

. . . . ⊙⊙

20 JULY

Does your body feel
balanced? If not, why?
What's weighing you down?

. . . .
. . . .
. . . .
. . . .
. . . .
. . . .
. . . .
. . . .
. . . .   ☺

21 JULY

Having patience is imperative
if you want to reap the
rewards of balance. Having
an understanding of the
lessons we may learn whilst
we're waiting is important,
too. Some things are just
worth waiting for.

. . . .
. . . .
. . . .
. . . .
. . . .
. . . .
. . . .
. . . .   ☺

22 JULY

Everyone deals with drama in different ways. For me, finding calm in life helps remedy this massively. Allow yourself time to stop and take stock so you can heal and repair from tough times.

....
....
....
....
....
....
....
....
....

23 JULY

It's give-yourself-a-break day. If you're trying to juggle too much, just let yourself off the hook and know it's OK for everything not to be perfect.

....
....
....
....
....
....
....
....
....

24 JULY

Don't feel guilty about saying 'no' to things. It's a hard one, I know. But if you choose to do one activity in life over another then there must be a good reason for that. Once you've made that decision, commit and don't feel the guilt! Guilt is a waste of energy.

JULY

25 JULY

Balance is an equation of patience, self-confidence and discipline. We'll naturally sway off it at times but if we know the route back, we'll be OK.

26 JULY

Don't get FOMO. It's pointless. Get what you can out of the decisions you've made without worrying what you're missing out on elsewhere.

27 JULY

The grass really isn't greener. We never know exactly what is going on for others and their lives even when we imagine we do.

. . . .
. . . .
. . . .
. . . .
. . . .
. . . .
. . . .
. . . .

28 JULY

Are you aware of social media disrupting your balance? If so, it's time for a digital detox day. Write here the switch on and off times. How long did you manage? And what did you do instead of checking your phone?

. . . .
. . . .
. . . .
. . . .
. . . .
. . . .
. . . .
. . . .

29 JULY

Rain or shine, spend at least one hour outside today. Find a park or a field and feel the grass between your toes. How does that feel?

30 JULY

What's your favourite summer anthem? How does it make you feel when you listen to it?

31 JULY

**THANK YOU
JULY FOR ...**

....

....

....

....

....

....

....

....

....

....

....

....

....

....

....

....

....

....

JULY

AUGUST

In August, I usually start to worry that summer is nearly over and I'll have to put away my flip-flops for another eight months and start eating excessive amounts of soup. I never feel ready. This way of thinking is never great for happiness as you're dreading the future but not enjoying the NOW either. So this month is all about the NOW. The power of simply enjoying the moment you're in. Accepting where you are in your life and its ever-changing shape, and what you have in this moment. It's so easy to get sidetracked by what we think we need or want, or how we wish we could change the past, but August can act as a good time to practice the deliciousness of NOW. Enjoy the sounds and smells around you and experience more fully what is really going on in you and around you. We, at times, miss so much of what is happening as we are so focused on other realms of time. We miss fleeting smiles, birds singing, intense tastes and moments of personal growth. Use this time to relax into NOW and see what you notice that you might have been missing.

1 AUGUST

Don't think about the past, or worry about the future this month. For me, bringing it back to the NOW is the key to calming nerves and enjoying life in real time. Time feels as if it almost slows down as you savour every inhale and exhale. Try it now.

· ·
· ·
· ·
· ·
· ·
· ·
· ·
· ·
· ·

2 AUGUST

The past can bring us so much joy as we recall rose-tinted memories of blissful times where worries didn't exist and the sun shone constantly. But it can also be a place full of regret that shouts so loudly you feel compelled to look back. Be honest about how it makes you feel here.

· ·
· ·
· ·
· ·
· ·
· ·
· ·
· ·

3   AUGUST

Most of us have moments, no matter how big or tiny, that affect us deeply. It's inevitable that we will all make mistakes and experience things that we wish we hadn't, but it's how much we let them affect our everyday lives that's important. Do we let these thoughts and stories define us? Or can we see them for what they are: moments. Slices of time that have occurred, had a directional purpose in our lives, then moved and changed into a new moment.

4   AUGUST

If you have uncomfortable memories, use the NOW to help you through. One deep breath, one moment where you notice how things feel, smell and look around you, one positive thought to combat the negative story and one second where you remember that right now, in this moment, everything is just fine.

5 AUGUST

What five memories make you beam to recall?

1
....

2
....

3
....

4
....

5
....

Enjoy the happiness of these memories.

6 AUGUST

I like to think of happy times
as perfume. The delicious and
intoxicating smell fades gradually until
you can't detect its notes at all. It was
beautiful, and all-encompassing, and
then it faded. That's why these good
times ARE so special – it's because
they have an expiration date. They
can't last for ever and they remain
dreamlike because they come to an
end. Embrace this fact and make
peace with it.

7 AUGUST

How do you feel about
the future? Does it fill you
with delicious excitement
or crazy dread? Write
down how you feel about
it here.

8 AUGUST

Aiming high and having
goals is exciting and buzzy.
We all get caught up in
the fantasy of the future
but daily happiness has to
come from the NOW.

....
....
....
....
....
....
....
....
....

9 AUGUST

The NOW is neutral. It
holds no overwhelming
emotion or concern.

....
....
....
....
....
....
....
....
....

10 AUGUST

Take a brief moment to recognise the NOW. Let your mind be completely free of the past and the future, and be aware of how you feel in this moment.

---

11 AUGUST

The singular thought I try to focus on in the tough times, the times of discomfort, is that this moment will expire. Like the cycle of day turning into night, or the circular motion of an inhaled and exhaled breath, this moment will come to a natural end.

12 AUGUST

Do you have a numbing tool? When you're trying to block out being in the NOW, do you reach for food, alcohol, gossip, or self-sabotage? We all do this! Recognising that we do it can be the step out to the other side. Write down your own numbing tool here and next time you reach for it, try and sit in the NOW instead.

13 AUGUST

Do you remember the summer holidays when you were a kid? Six whole weeks off school, which felt like six months? Kids live in the moment, enjoying each fun pastime then moving on to the next one. Now time seems to whizz by because we are constantly looking ahead. We can slow down our experience and savour what life has to offer if we just sit in the NOW, a little more often.

"

HAPPINESS IS ACHIEVED WHEN YOU STOP WAITING FOR IT AND MAKE THE MOST OF THE MOMENT YOU ARE IN NOW

"

14 AUGUST

The wonderful thing is, finding awareness in a moment of panic, fear, or worry could be just enough to break the circle of negative personal habits and patterns.

· ·

· ·

· ·

· ·

· ·

· ·

· ·

· ·

15 AUGUST

What we do doesn't make us who we are.

· ·

· ·

· ·

· ·

· ·

· ·

· ·

· ·

16 AUGUST

When we try to squeeze the life out of a good moment, we hinder its ability to breathe and drift in and out of our lives naturally. We must have faith that more of these divine love bubbles will float into our lives again.

17 AUGUST

We can all learn from the past. Write down your own lesson in the balloons and imagine them floating away.

18 AUGUST

Dreading future plans or
situations can heap anxiety and
fear right into your lap. If there's
something that's worrying you,
share it here. What can you
do or change to help diminish
this fear? If you can't make any
changes, accept that, but know
you DO have the strength and
determination to get through
what is ahead.

19 AUGUST

In the present, our minds are
clearer and not crammed tight
with past and future anxieties.
We can make decisions from
a place of clarity and feel
calm even when things seem
chaotic around us. Stress is
reduced and the feeling of being
overwhelmed fades into the
background. To me, that feels
like a happy place to be.

20 AUGUST

For the next week, let's really get our minds noticing the NOW. Pick a spot at a window you can open (or in the garden if you have one and you're confident about the weather!). Then, each day go to your Now place and write down everything you can see, smell, hear and taste around you.

....
....
....
....
....
....
....
....
....

21 AUGUST

DAY 1

....
....
....
....
....
....
....
....
....

22 AUGUST

DAY 2

....
....
....
....
....
....
....
.... (••)

---

23 AUGUST

DAY 3

....
....
....
....
....
....
....
.... (••)

24 AUGUST

DAY 4

· ·
· ·
· ·
· ·
· ·
· ·
· ·
· ·
· ☺

25 AUGUST

DAY 5

· ·
· ·
· ·
· ·
· ·
· ·
· ·
· ☺

AUGUST

26 AUGUST

DAY 6

AUGUST

27 AUGUST

DAY 7

. . . .

. . . .

. . . .

. . . .

. . . .

. . . .

. . . .

. . . . ☺

28 AUGUST

Reaching the end of the
rainbow doesn't mean
you'll be met by a better
version of yourself.
Getting happy NOW
means you'll enjoy the
whole journey a lot more!

. . . .

. . . .

. . . .

. . . .

. . . .

. . . . ☺

29 AUGUST

Be ready for the good
and bad times with open
arms, knowing they'll exist
and then expire. In the
meantime, all we can do is
be in the NOW and take
that big look around us.

. . . .

. . . .

. . . .

. . . .

. . . .

. . . .

. . . .

. . . .

30 AUGUST

The end of the summer
is almost here. Enjoy the
last heat of the month,
even the warm rain. Feel
it, store up that memory
for the winter months to
come. Be in the NOW.

. . . .

. . . .

. . . .

. . . .

. . . .

. . . .

. . . .

. . . .

"

THE SECRET TO 'HAVING IT ALL' IS BELIEVING YOU ALREADY DO

"

31 AUGUST

**THANK YOU
AUGUST FOR ...**

AUGUST

SEPTEMBER

I always feel very creative in September. I'm a September baby, and my daughter was born shortly after my birthday, so there's always lots of celebration and creativity. From getting arty and crafty for our joint birthday party, to taking more time to write and paint as the evenings draw in, I feel inspired and settled into a creative flow more than ever. Maybe this also harks back to when we were at school. Perhaps you are still studying and get that buzz of a new pencil case packed with shiny pens and new erasers. All of those pens and pencils just waiting to be broken in. Heaven! Use this month to flex your creative muscles. Maybe you don't feel you have a single creative bone in your body. Well, you certainly will have, you just might not have found it yet! You don't have to be good artistically to be creative, you just have to be willing to let it flow out of you. Whether it's music, art, writing, movement, gardening or creating in your home, at work, at school or simply in your head. We all have the ability to create stories, ideas and beauty! Let that creativity flow ...

1 SEPTEMBER

Just write. Write whatever comes spilling out and feel the creativity of just letting go.

· ·
· ·
· ·
· ·
· ·
· ·
· ·
· ⌣

2 SEPTEMBER

Write to someone explaining what it is you love about them. I adore the creativity of writing a letter with pen and paper rather than compiling an email.

· ·
· ·
· ·
· ·
· ·
· ·
· ·
· ⌣

3 SEPTEMBER

What makes you tick creatively? Is it writing, drawing, sewing, telling stories, thinking up ideas, solving problems, gardening, sport? Write all of your favourite creative activities in this space.

....
....
....
....
....
....
....
....
....

4 SEPTEMBER

Creating my children is something I'm still in awe of – I feel proud about it every day. I feel so grateful for them and still feel completely astounded that they grew in my belly. I also feel incredibly happy looking at paintings I've created. Even if the painting isn't the best work I've done, I love that my ideas and thoughts have materialised onto a canvas. What are you proud of creating and why?

....
....
....
....
....
....
....
....

5 SEPTEMBER

Create something today. Whether it's a drawing, a story or simply an idea in your head for something new. Get creative, feel the flow.

....

....

....

....

....

....

....

....

6 SEPTEMBER

Who are your favourite creators? Do you have creative heroes who inspire you and push you on in your own creative exploration? I have a huge list of music artists, painters and thinkers who inspire me greatly.

....

....

....

....

....

....

....

....

7 SEPTEMBER

Make today all about
creating delicious food.
Perhaps some late-night
baking or a yummy home-
made lunch before you set
off for the day.

8 SEPTEMBER

Create some headspace for yourself. Being creative requires being in the right mental space, so make sure you give yourself the time to just BE rather than constantly needing to DO.

9 SEPTEMBER

Create a lovely atmosphere for yourself tonight. Candles, music and good company. Creating a nice space and sanctuary for yourself helps the creative juices flow.

10 SEPTEMBER

What's your favourite book and how does it make you feel? I often feel very buzzed creatively when I've read a great book. I feel open to new possibilities and excited about what's possible.

....
....
....
....
....
....
....
....

11 SEPTEMBER

Create your own list of life rules, rules that feel right to you. Why follow the pack when we know it'll never make us happy? This is always a comfort when you feel left out or like you're going about things in a different way to others.

....
....
....
....
....
....
....

12 SEPTEMBER

Draw a picture here.
Doodle, fill the space
and see what is waiting
to come out of your
imagination.

13 SEPTEMBER

Need inspiration? Jump
on to Pinterest and look
for ideas and images that
fill you with joy. I love to
make boards that help me
stay focused on ideas I
want to put into action.

14 SEPTEMBER

Try something new. Do you feel you're lacking creativity in your life? Is there a hobby you'd love to try? Learning a language or dancing or knitting? GO FOR IT!

15 SEPTEMBER

The feeling of being in your creative flow is unbeatable. I get the biggest kick out of being creative, whether it's writing, painting or baking cakes. The process of focusing on the task at hand, and knowing there'll be a result at the end, thrills me deeply.

16 SEPTEMBER

Create a mess while you're cooking. Let the kitchen get splattered and covered and get into the groove of letting that food come to life. When I cook with my kids, we create sheer havoc and it's so much fun. I am a bit strange in the fact that I don't mind tidying it all up at the end either. Creating order is one of my go-to habits when I feel a bit all over the place.

"

HAPPINESS IS
HANDMADE

"

17   SEPTEMBER

If I'm feeling a little low, I'll put together an outfit that empowers me and helps me along my way. Creating new exciting fashion looks might not fix us, but it can help to express how we are feeling to the outside world. If I'm feeling quiet, I'll blend in with the crowd, whereas if I'm feeling confident, I'll burst wth colours and clashing prints.

18   SEPTEMBER

Need clothing inspiration? Head to your local second-hand shop and find that gem. I LOVE a bargain and something that no one else will have. If you haven't done it before, it will feel like a proper adventure, but second-hand clothes have a story and a character that new clothes simply can't emulate. They're as unique as you.

19 SEPTEMBER

Create joy for another.
Send a friend a lovely
note or postcard in the
post, which will be a total
surprise. Once my friend
sent me a balloon with a
note attached to it in a
box rather than a letter
and it kept me buzzing
for weeks. Spread some
happiness.

20 SEPTEMBER

Create space in your diary
... for yourself. Don't feel
you always have to be
socialising and cramming
in activities every day. It's
just as important to have
blank diary days to take
stock and just be.

21 SEPTEMBER

Have you ever customised an item of clothing? It needn't look childish or naff. There are so many ways to up-cycle clothing these days, from fabric paint and dyes, pins and patches to studs and lace. Look online for inspiration and have fun with the whole creative process.

22 SEPTEMBER

Make your own cards to give to friends. It could be thank-you cards that you keep ready for the right moment, birthday cards for loved ones or party invites for an upcoming event. You don't have to be good at art and will most definitely save yourself a fortune.

23 SEPTEMBER

I always have my best creative ideas when I'm out walking or running. My head is simply trying to keep me going, and not give up, so it feels pretty clear and worry-free. This is when ideas will pop into my head for my books and design work. Give physical movement a go.

24 SEPTEMBER

What have you created today?

· ·

· ·

· ·

· ·

· ·

· ·

· ·

· ◡◡

25 SEPTEMBER

You've almost completed
a month of magic-making.
How does it feel to look
back at your creativity?

· ·

· ·

· ·

· ·

· ·

· ·

· ◡◡

26 SEPTEMBER

The seasons are changing – does this bring a change in your feelings? Take stock here.

....
....
....
....
....
....
....
....

27 SEPTEMBER

We often have such fond memories stored away on our phones, and sometimes forgotten, in the form of selfies and photos with friends. Can you create a happy photo folder? It can be a paper one with printed photos or just a special folder on your phone, to remember the happy times you've experienced. Have them ready for that moment you need to count your blessings and feel the love.

....
....
....
....
....
....
....

28 SEPTEMBER

Can you get creative with someone else? With a best mate or your kids? Often being rubbish at something together, and learning together, can make for fun. It can also help with letting go of perfect. We've all got to start somewhere.

· ·

· ·

· ·

· ·

· ·

· ·

· ·

· ·

29 SEPTEMBER

Have you created any unwanted drama this month? Write it down here, accept it and see how you might do things differently next month.

· ·

· ·

· ·

· ·

· ·

· ·

· ·

"

EAT

SLEEP

CREATE

"

30 SEPTEMBER

**THANK YOU
SEPTEMBER FOR ...**

SEPTEMBER

OCTOBER

I love this cosy month with its golden leaves and wholesome warm food. I feel instantly nourished whilst thinking about it. October signifies autumn and a shift for us all. Changes in season can sometimes be an unwelcome reminder that we are dealing with change constantly. We are navigating around our children growing older, our own bodies working differently and morphing with age, our friends moving, ideas changing, social concepts shifting, birth, death, marriage, divorce. Change is inevitable and can be hard to deal with. Even change that seems positive can take its toll as we humans naturally aren't that good at it. We feel discomfort and uncertainty around things not being quite the same. So let's all use this month to accept and embrace change. This is a time to look at our lives and how malleable we are in our surroundings. October is about being conscious of change and what it means to us all.

1 OCTOBER

Change can be hard. What upcoming changes are worrying you?

. . . .

. . . .

. . . .

. . . .

. . . .

. . . .

. . . .

. . . . ⊙‿

2 OCTOBER

Change can also be good. What life changes could you make to create some more balance or happiness?

. . . .

. . . .

. . . .

. . . .

. . . .

. . . .

. . . . ⊙‿

OCTOBER

3 OCTOBER

How might you take steps
towards the change you
thought of yesterday?

. . . .

. . . .

. . . .

. . . .

. . . .

. . . .

. . . .

. . . .

. . . .

4 OCTOBER

Change needn't be mighty
great leaps; tiny steps
are equally as important
and incredibly powerful.
Getting stuck in a situation
is debilitating and stops
you from personal growth.
Take small steps and know
big changes will come.

. . . .

. . . .

. . . .

. . . .

. . . .

. . . .

. . . .

5 OCTOBER

Which changes this year
have left you feeling
unstable? Have you
experienced unwanted
change and how are you
dealing with it?

....
....
....
....
....
....
....
....
....

6 OCTOBER

Put on David Bowie
'Changes', turn the
volume up and listen to
the words. Magic.

....
....
....
....
....
....
....
....
....

7 OCTOBER

Have you ever tried to change someone? Have you realised how impossible and pointless this is? If someone in life grates against your own beliefs, try changing your own tolerance and acceptance rather than trying to change something that you can't. This can be hard but so liberating on the path to happiness.

8 OCTOBER

What positive changes have
you made in life and where
have they led you to?

....
....
....
....
....
....
....
....
.... ☺

9 OCTOBER

Get cosy. Embrace this
change of season and
enjoy every bit of this
snuggly month.

....
....
....
....
....
....
....
....
.... ☺

10 OCTOBER

Cook a delicious stew or hearty soup for dinner. This time of year is so perfect for warming meals that satisfy and soothe you.

11 OCTOBER

What changes would you like to make to yourself? Rather than focusing on these changes, can you start to accept those parts of you and learn to like them?

12 OCTOBER

Change can be tough for kids. If you
have young ones in the family, try
talking to them about how change makes
them feel. My own son can get pretty
grumpy about certain changes in life,
which I've learned to realise is related
to his frustration at not yet being able
to articulate how they make him feel.
Communicating is always the best
medicine in challenging situations.

13 OCTOBER

Change your speed of life. If you're
someone who rushes from place to
place, trying to achieve too much and
ending up wearing yourself out, try
stopping and letting go a little more. If
you are someone who gets stuck in slow
motion with a neverending to-do list
that doesn't get done, try kick-starting
yourself into action by choosing the
easiest job off the list to complete.
You'll feel a huge achievement at ticking
one thing off. Tiny steps.

14 OCTOBER

Do you have any heroes in
life that have made great
changes to social issues,
the arts, or charities you
believe in? If so, who are
they and why do you
admire them?

....
....
....
....
....
....
....
....
....

15 OCTOBER

Do you believe you can
make positive changes for
someone else? If so, who
is the individual or group
of people and how can
you help?

....
....
....
....
....
....
....
....

16 OCTOBER

Do you feel irate when people are rude? Do you fly off the handle when you're misunderstood? Do you break down when you feel insecure and hurt? How can you change your perspective on the matter and see the bigger picture?

....
....
....
....
....
....
....
....

17 OCTOBER

Draw a picture of what change means to you here.

18 OCTOBER

Can you switch up how you get to work or school? Is there a new person you could travel in with? A new way of getting there? Can you walk or cycle and set off that bit earlier? I used to love walking in to Radio 1 even though it took well over an hour. I would pop on my headphones and start my day with energy and headspace.

19 OCTOBER

Ever wanted to change up your career but felt too scared? I've felt like this throughout my career. I've gone from lots of job security to a more adventurous path with none. All I know is that when I've followed my gut, I feel a whole lot better.

20 OCTOBER

Are there any small tweaks you can make to your relationship for the better? Is there an opportunity for a regular date night, even if it's watching the same show together? Can you ditch your phones and have a sit-down dinner a couple of times a week? What small changes do you think would benefit you?

21 OCTOBER

Change is so good for the soul as we get to experience different parts of ourselves that we may not have focused on previously. We get to expand emotionally and learn a little more about ourselves each time.

22 OCTOBER

Are you good at change or
do you prefer routine? I'm
not a fan of routine at all so
always strive for adventure
when I can. I am quite
strict with routine when it
comes to my kids though,
as I feel more in control of
what, at times, feels like
sheer chaos.

23 OCTOBER

Try using pumpkin in
your meals this week.
It's everywhere at this
time of year and so so
delicious. Pumpkin pies,
tarts, gnocchi, there are so
many dreamy options.

24 OCTOBER

Get cosy with mates. As
the nights draw in, organise
a relaxed evening of food
and laughter. A glowing
fire and candles will usually
help proceedings too.

. . . .

. . . .

. . . .

. . . .

. . . .

. . . .

. . . .

. . . .

25 OCTOBER

What changes have
happened in your life that
you're grateful for?

. . . .

. . . .

. . . .

. . . .

. . . .

. . . .

. . . .

. . . .

26 OCTOBER

The clocks change and this
can be a tough time of the
year as the nights are darker.
Look for the positive: what
can you do with the extra
hour you gain?

27 OCTOBER

How can you make the
darker evenings more
joyful?

....
....
....
....
....
....
....
....
....

28 OCTOBER

Orange is often
seen as the colour of
transformation. Close
your eyes and picture a
glowing orange ball. Let it
remind you that change is
ok and that you are safe.

....
....
....
....
....
....
....
....

29 OCTOBER

Have you felt happiness today? Have the small changes you've made this month brought a fresh openness to the emotion?

30 OCTOBER

Tomorrow is Halloween! In my twenties I saw it as an opportunity to party, but when I was living alone I was nervous to open the door to trick-or-treaters. Nowadays it's all about the kids dressing up and having fun. What's your plan for the night? Be aware of what brings you joy.

31 OCTOBER

**THANK YOU
OCTOBER FOR ...**

OCTOBER

NOVEMBER

This month is about community and family. Blood-related or not, it's a time to gather. Huddle and be close to those you can lean on and those you feel you can support. It's about comfort and relaxing into the arms of those you know cradle you and it's a time to feel gratitude for that. Whether it's for a firework display, some cosy cooking on a wet Sunday or settling down to watch a box set with loved ones, enjoy the company and soak up the love. If you have ever experienced feeling alone or do currently, I urge you to seek out this love as it'll be there for you. Whether it's a local community or group of like-minded people, you may find them through a new hobby or perhaps by trying something new socially. Gather with food, huddle around for laughter, and feel the embrace of those around you. November needn't be so cold!

1 NOVEMBER

How do you fit into your own family and what role do you play? Sometimes we subconsciously give ourselves roles within this unit and that can change our behaviour for the better or worse when we are with our families. Are you the antagonist? The carer? The victim? The mediator? What is your role and how does it make you feel?

. . . .
. . . .
. . . .
. . . .
. . . .
. . . .
. . . .
. . . . ⊙‿⊙

2 NOVEMBER

Family doesn't have to be about blood relatives. You can feel at home in any group of people who make you feel supported.

. . . .
. . . .
. . . .
. . . .
. . . .
. . . .
. . . .
. . . . ⊙‿⊙

3   NOVEMBER

When you're with your
family, how do you feel?

· ·
· ·
· ·
· ·
· ·
· ·
· ·
· ·
· ☺

4   NOVEMBER

What is your favourite
family memory to recall?
Is it a snapshot from
your childhood or a more
recent moment?

· ·
· ·
· ·
· ·
· ·
· ·
· ☺

5   NOVEMBER

Gather with friends or family
and cook some food together.
If you don't have outdoor
space or a local firework
display, simply make this a
night for sharing and cosiness
with people you love. If you
can, write your name in the air
with a sparkler. There is magic
and joy in the simple things.
And you matter too.

· ·

· ·

· ·

· ·

· ·

· ·

· ·

· ☺

6   NOVEMBER

If you're a tired parent,
remember to stop and
pat yourself on the
back today. It's rare
anyone else will, so take
a moment to remember
how much you do and
how brilliant you are!

· ·

· ·

· ·

· ·

· ·

· ·

· ☺

7 NOVEMBER

Being a parent is magical yet simultaneously tough. You face challenges every day and learn a lot about yourself. The constant task at hand involves a lot of caring, nurturing and organising and sometimes we forget to have fun in the midst of it all. See if you can find time for fun today, even if it's an hour where you break off from your usual routine for a burst of laughter. I always try to remember, in the chaos of parenting, that my family won't suddenly fall apart if I take my foot off the gas for half an hour.

8 NOVEMBER

Call a friend today to tell them you appreciate their friendship. Having a gang of like-minded souls in your life is a gift. Why not let them know about it?

. . . .

. . . .

. . . .

. . . .

. . . .

. . . .

. . . .

. . . . ⊙‿⊙

9 NOVEMBER

I feel very lucky to have a wonderfully eccentric gang of mates in my life. Some from childhood, some I've made at work and some brilliant individuals who have just floated into my life at the right time. Who are you grateful for?

. . . .

. . . .

. . . .

. . . .

. . . .

. . . .

. . . .

. . . . ⊙‿⊙

10 NOVEMBER

Friendships bring joy but the wrong ones can bring pain. Are there any toxic friendships in your life that you think aren't working for you any more. Are you holding on to a friendship out of fear rather than the loyal happiness it brings?

11 NOVEMBER

Are you a good friend? What makes you a brilliant mate? If you have any self-doubt, what could you do to become a better friend?

12 NOVEMBER

When were you last
helped out by a friend and
how did it feel?

· ·

· ·

· ·

· ·

· ·

· ·

· ·

· ⌣

13 NOVEMBER

When did you last help a
friend out and how did it
make you feel?

· ·

· ·

· ·

· ·

· ·

· ·

· ·

· ⌣

14 NOVEMBER

Stick a photo here of you and a friend. Describe your friend in three words and write them by your photo.

. . . .

. . . .

. . . .

15 NOVEMBER

Be open to new friendship. You're never too old to make new friends. New acquaintances can teach us a lot and bring out new qualities in us.

. . . .

. . . .

. . . .

. . . .

. . . .

. . . .

. . . .

. . . .

16 NOVEMBER

Plan a road trip for the future. Even if it's just a day out somewhere you've never been before. I spent four days on the road with some new friends from work recently as we were filming up and down the UK. We played Dolly Parton very loudly and sang and laughed the whole way. Road trips are always a hoot.

17 NOVEMBER

Have a Netflix night with a mate. Getting cosy on the sofa with good snacks and a wonderful friend is unbeatable. You don't have to go out to have a great time. November for me is all about staying in and snuggling up to people I love.

18 NOVEMBER

What friendships have you
lost over the years and why?

. . . .
. . . .
. . . .
. . . .
. . . .
. . . .
. . . .
. . . .
. . . .

19 NOVEMBER

Saying sorry is incredibly powerful.
An apology not only allows others
to know that you are aware of
your personal misdemeanours
but you also free yourself from
the ties to the situation. You may
not be instantly forgiven, and the
situation may not be forgotten,
but you have made a goodwill
transaction and released yourself
from the grips of guilt. Do you
owe anyone an apology?

. . . .
. . . .
. . . .
. . . .
. . . .
. . . .
. . . .

20 NOVEMBER

Does anyone owe you an apology? Maybe you don't want to get in contact with this person ever again, but writing down your thoughts about your own experience of pain can be very freeing. Write a letter here that you may never send. Write it to the person that hurt you and forgive them. Free yourself from the resentment and anger and get all of those unspoken words out of your head.

21 NOVEMBER

Hug your loved ones that bit tighter today. And when you say goodbye, make 'I love you' the last thing you say to them. How easy do you find that to do?

22 NOVEMBER

Meeting a new friend can feel very much like falling in love. That inexplicable feeling of connecting with someone on a deeper level and knowing they'll bring light into your life.

23 NOVEMBER

Smile at a stranger
and feel the ripples of
happiness fan out.

. . . .

. . . .

. . . .

. . . .

. . . .

. . . .

. . . .

24 NOVEMBER

Make someone you love
a cake or if you are not a
keen baker perhaps just
a handmade gift or card.
Receiving gifts when it's
not your birthday is such
a treat and handing them
over feels pretty great too.

. . . .

. . . .

. . . .

. . . .

. . . .

. . . .

. . . .

25 NOVEMBER

Look back at old photos of
you and your friends and
laugh from the belly. I love
looking back at old school
photos and girls' holidays!
Some dodgy outfits, hilarious
memories and good reason
to reminisce and remember
the fun times. Laughter
feeds my soul – we have to
make time for it.

26 NOVEMBER

Have someone over for
weekend breakfast or brunch.
It can be a drag to go out at
night when it's cold in the
winter, or feel overwhelmed
by a dinner invite, so having
friends over for eggs and
pancakes in the morning can
be fun instead. They can pile
over in their PJ's and drink tea
with you while you cook. Bliss.

27 NOVEMBER

Don't forget to find the friendship in your relationship. If you have a partner and you've been together for a long time, it is easy to get caught up in the logistics of life and your own rhythms. It's always important to remember the friendship that lies beneath it all. Laughing and chatting about subjects that aren't family-based or work-based, and going somewhere outside of your home is a good way of breaking down those barriers.

28 NOVEMBER

Remember back in
February when you wrote
down who your 'calm'
friend was and why? Give
them a call today and tell
them all the lovely things
you wrote about them.

29 NOVEMBER

Choose your favourite
family photo and have it
printed. Give a copy to
everyone in the photo you
can. Write on the back
why you love it and them.

30 NOVEMBER

**THANK YOU
NOVEMBER FOR ...**

NOVEMBER

DECEMBER

I bet, like me, you're thinking, 'Well, where did that year go?' Another year flies past and leaves us with new lessons learned and new information stored. How do you feel about the last 12 months? This is the perfect month to slow down a little and take stock of what you have experienced over the course of a year. Was it a good year? Full of wonderful change, happy memories and loved ones? Or perhaps it was a little dull or a little dark? Maybe you can gain a little positivity from seeking out what you have learned from the experiences, no matter how tough or bleak. I have looked back on some years with fondness and love and others I've filed under 'Erase' but I'll be able to eventually see the good that came out of it all. It is obviously harder to extract the positive sometimes when you've experienced something negative, but if you use this month to stop and take stock, you might just see that silver lining. Unwind, take a moment in this busy month and digest it all, along with the Christmas dinner.

1 DECEMBER

December can seem like a crazy month with shopping to get done, endless lists, Christmas work parties and family gatherings. Carve out some time, however short, to start the wind-down to the holidays. If you're feeling mentally prepared and relaxed, this month will be a joy and not a dread.

. . . .
. . . .
. . . .
. . . .
. . . .
. . . .
. . . .
. . . .

2 DECEMBER

Can you slow down a little this month? Is there room for some rest and down-time to bring some calm to the end of the year?

. . . .
. . . .
. . . .
. . . .
. . . .
. . . .
. . . .
. . . .

3   DECEMBER

How do you best like to wind down? List your four favourite ways here.

....
....
....
....
....
....
....
....
....

4   DECEMBER

Sometimes I give myself a hard time and don't feel I deserve to take a break. I feel like I should keep trying to do my best and eventually get worn out. We all deserve a break, whether it be from the physical strains of life or the mental. Give yourself permission to relax.

....
....
....
....
....
....
....
....

5 DECEMBER

Make some festive food. I
love getting excited about
Christmas so my festive
baking starts early in the
month. Gingerbread or
spicy loaf cakes are perfect
winter warmers. They fill
the house with delicious,
spicy, happy smells.

· ·
· ·
· ·
· ·
· ·
· ·
· ·
· ·

6 DECEMBER

This time of year can be
awfully tough for some. If you
have lost someone around
Christmastime, or experienced
pain or trauma, this can be an
evocative month for all the
wrong reasons. If you know
someone who has a tough
time in December, and feels
particularly lonely or isolated,
see how you might be able to
ease the pain.

· ·
· ·
· ·
· ·
· ·
· ·
· ·

7 DECEMBER

This month can be overwhelming. Use this page to write a list of all the things you need to do before 25th December. Is it a shopping list, a note to get in touch with family abroad or perhaps a list of work that needs to be done? Use it to gain some much-needed clarity.

8   DECEMBER

If you celebrate Christmas
with your family, is there
anyone you could invite over
who you know doesn't have
anyone to share it with? Most
years we have friends over
who are on their own or are
from overseas and we make
them an honorary member of
the family for the day.

....
....
....
....
....
....
....
....
.... ⊙‿⊙

9   DECEMBER

Make some handmade
Christmas cards. So much
more fun, especially if you
have kids to help out. They
don't have to be fancy
or overly decadent, just
enjoy the process and love
the glittery outcome.

....
....
....
....
....
....
....
....
.... ⊙‿⊙

10 DECEMBER

Have an early night. Enjoy the early nightfall and take the opportunity to catch up on some zzz's. Spray some lavender on your pillow, turn your phone off way before you hit the sack and enjoy some sleepy rejuvenation.

....
....
....
....
....
....
....
....
....

11 DECEMBER

If you are working over Christmas, why not throw an early party now? Get your loved ones over to yours for a mulled wine or perhaps go out for a drink with some friends so you feel you've had your chance to say cheers to December and talk about the year.

....
....
....
....
....
....
....
....

12 DECEMBER

Send someone in hospital a Christmas card. There are some wonderful initiatives and charities where you can send a card or gift to someone who will be in hospital over the festive period. Post Pals (www.postpals.co.uk) is an excellent charity where you can send cards and gifts to children in hospital and put a smile on their faces. It's such an easy thing to do and helps families going through tough times so much.

13 DECEMBER

Wear something red. I love the vibrancy that the colour red brings around this time of year. It feels bursting with love, cheer and festivities. Even if it's just a lipstick or your nails or socks! Go for it.

14 DECEMBER

Looking back isn't
necessarily a bad thing
to do. This year, living in
the NOW has been so
important but it's also
important to look back
and digest what you have
been through. If we have
experienced tough times
we might feel we want
to brush them under the
carpet and not think about
them again. This usually
leads to them popping
up when you're least
expecting them to bite you
on the arse. I much prefer
to look back, digest and
then process how to accept
tough times. Look them in
the eye, then move on free
from their memory.

15 DECEMBER

Go for a wintry walk. Get
bundled up in a jumper and
scarf and big boots and
head outside. Even better,
walk with friends if you can.
It's a chance to chat and
catch up and you'll have
lovely rosy cheeks to boot
by the end.

....
....
....
....
....
....
....
....
....

16 DECEMBER

Kiss someone under the
mistletoe.

....
....
....
....
....
....
....
....
....

17 DECEMBER

Skype a friend who lives far away. I love FaceTiming or Skyping friends who live out of town or abroad at Christmas. It feels much more personal than a text or email. For some people it can be hard to make that initial connection but I think it's always a feel-good thing to do.

18 DECEMBER

Listening as well as talking is so good for the soul. When we are with a group of friends, it can be easy to fall into the swing of talking at people or telling too many stories. A tip I learned for good listening: don't think about what you're going to say next. Just let your friend speak and pause. Try it, there's a real magical art to being a good listener and I love practising every day.

19 DECEMBER

Lonely is not happy. If you are single, have recently moved or just don't happen to be around many loved ones, don't let loneliness dominate your Christmas. There'll be someone out there waiting to befriend you or help you out. Try something new like a local activity or class or volunteering and make a connection. Sometimes making new friends later in life can feel like hard work but it's so worth it. Be filled with a sense of adventure and be brave, the world will give back to you.

20 DECEMBER

Go ice-skating. I haven't done this for years but it's always on my wish list for Dec! I know I'll laugh loads, get the blood pumping and definitely fall over!

. . . .
. . . .
. . . .
. . . .
. . . .
. . . .
. . . .
. . . .

21 DECEMBER

What's on your Christmas wish list? I'm not talking about presents or material things. What do you really want for the end of the year? How do you want to feel and what moves do you want to make?

. . . .
. . . .
. . . .
. . . .
. . . .
. . . .
. . . .
. . . .

22 DECEMBER

Listen to the sounds around you. Steal the moment and take in the smells and noises. Clear your head and just feel what is going on nearby. Give yourself as long as you need in this space.

23 DECEMBER

At Christmastime, I love to have a pan bubbling away on the stove with some oranges, cloves and cinnamon in some water. It's not something edible or drinkable, it's simply to make the house smell amazing and very festive. It's great while you're watching a Christmas movie too.

"

IT DOESN'T
MATTER WHAT'S
BEEN WRITTEN
IN YOUR STORY
SO FAR, IT'S
HOW YOU FILL
UP THE REST OF
THE PAGES THAT
COUNTS

"

24 DECEMBER

Open up your imagination. For kids this time of year is all about fantasy and imagination so don't forget to flex yours now you're that bit older. Dream big and open your mind to fantasy. Believe everything is possible.

25 DECEMBER

HAPPY CHRISTMAS!

What happened today that
made you smile?

26 DECEMBER

Don't feel the guilt.
Sometimes Boxing Day
can be a time for guilt
as December can be a
decadent month. Don't
worry if you ate too
much, drank too much or
received gifts you didn't
think you deserved. Just
feel the gratitude for it all.

27 DECEMBER

These days are the inbetweeners of the year. You may have some time off work now or have more family around to help with the kids. So why not use this time to take stock of your emotions? How has this year made you feel?

....
....
....
....
....
....
....
....
....

28 DECEMBER

And use this space to list your highlights of the year...

....
....
....
....
....
....
....
....
....

29 DECEMBER

Life is never smooth and often we are shaping happiness and calm from the madness of the daily chaos. What would you change about the year? What could bring more happiness next year?

. . . .

. . . .

. . . .

. . . .

. . . .

. . . .

. . . .

. . . .

30 DECEMBER

What were your lows of the year? What did you learn about yourself from them? Write here how you can work on not repeating the sadness of the past.

. . . .

. . . .

. . . .

. . . .

. . . .

. . . .

. . . .

. . . .

31 DECEMBER

Now say goodbye and thank you to this year. If it was a tough year, say thanks for the lessons learned and personal expansion. In the gratitude comes growth. From personal growth comes self-knowledge and with that, you really are on the path to inviting more happiness into your life.

. . . .

. . . .

. . . .

. . . .

. . . .

. . . .

. . . .

. . . .

. . . .

. . . .

. . . .

. . . .

. . . .

. . . .

. . . .

. . . .

SO, THANK YOU 20__ FOR ...

....

....

....

....

....

....

....

....

....

....

....

....

....

....

....

NOTES

· ·

· ·

· ·

· ·

· ·

· ·

· ·

· ·

· ·

· ·

· ·

· ·

· ·

· ·

· ·

NOTES

....

....

....

....

....

....

....

....

....

....

....

....

....

....

....

NOTES

. . . .

. . . .

. . . .

. . . .

. . . .

. . . .

. . . .

. . . .

. . . .

. . . .

. . . .

. . . .

. . . .

. . . .

. . . .

. . . .

NOTES

· ·

· ·

· ·

· ·

· ·

· ·

· ·

· ·

· ·

· ·

· ·

· ·

· ·

· ·

· ·

· ·

NOTES

· ·

· ·

· ·

· ·

· ·

· ·

· ·

· ·

· ·

· ·

· ·

· ·

· ·

· ·

· ·

NOTES

....
....
....
....
....
....
....
....
....
....
....
....
....
....
....

NOTES

· ·

· ·

· ·

· ·

· ·

· ·

· ·

· ·

· ·

· ·

· ·

· ·

· ·

· ·

· ·

· ·